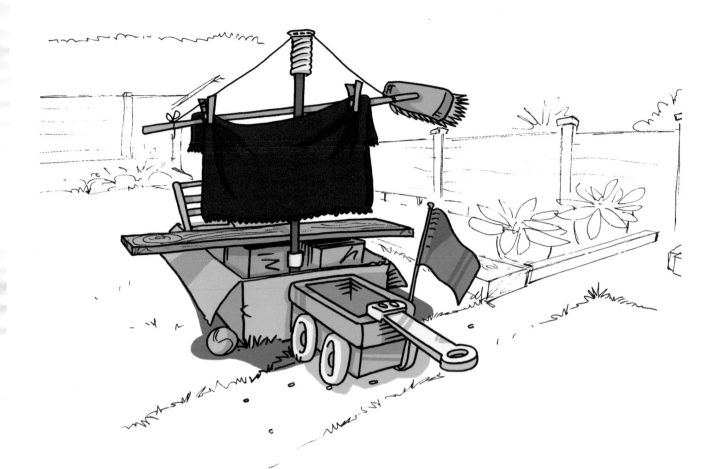

Tom has a ship on the grass.

1

The ship has a mast, a
sail and a flag.

Tom has a plank to stand on. Tom has fun.

Bella is in the ship with Tom.

Tom tells Bella to get on the plank.

Bella steps on the plank.

Bella has fun.

Tom jumps off the plank.

The plank tips up.

Bump! Bang! Crash!

Bella is on the grass.